I NEVER GOT TO HOLD YOU

ART THERAPY AND JOURNALING ACTIVITIES
FOR THOSE WHO HAVE MISCARRIED

CONNIE PRUITT

Connie Pruitt

I Never Got To Hold You

I have decided that the only way to live is to embrace grief. For grief only exists where love lived first.

–Franchesca Cox

In loving memory of my three heavenly babies.

Table of Contents

Preface

Please allow me to express my deepest sympathy if you are reading this book because you are grieving the loss of a baby. I can only hope the words and activities that follow will help you recover a bit faster, bring you comfort, and create memories of your sweet baby.

If you are reading this because you know someone that lost a baby and want to help, this book will better equip you to understand the grief they are experiencing and learn how you can be a part of the caring movement called "The Knitted Blanket". Chapter 14 will give you insight on what to say and do to help those who are grieving the loss of a baby.

Chapter 1

The Hardest Goodbye

There is a unique pain that comes from preparing a place in your heart for a child that never comes.

— *David Platt*

I've been here before. As I write this, I have a *déjà vu* moment of sorts. Of trying to write down words of comfort to help me. To help others. Then I realize it's not *déjà vu* at all. My younger self started this book many times over the years. After my first miscarriage.

For so long, I didn't talk about it. I felt I shouldn't talk about it. It made others uncomfortable. They didn't know how to respond, and that just made it worse. I didn't want to make anyone feel weird about my situation—better to suppress it. After all, you can't explain the level of grief you are feeling to someone that hasn't experienced the loss of a baby, right? So instead of talking about it, I would privately write and draw my feelings out, in hopes of someday putting them on pages like this.

The topic of grief has resonated in my soul because of the lasting impact of my own experiences with the grief in my life. But then I turned my grief into curiosity. And that curiosity has led me here.

This book was written in the hopes of helping others understand the deep sadness they may be feeling. Fresh grief that needs a place to go. I only hope the following pages can soften that grief.

It's important to note that I am not a medical doctor or psychologist. I'm just one woman that became obsessed with researching how the brain reacts to grief in order to help myself heal through art therapy. The art therapy-based activities in this book are included to enhance your own, personal healing process.

Chapter 1 Art Therapy Activity: Messages to Myself

Sometimes it helps to jot down how you feel into words, pictures, or both. When you are overwhelmed by the grief you may be experiencing, try drawing how you feel to help you deal with it in a more productive way. It's a great way to organize your thoughts by priority, fears, and concerns. If you write them down as you experience feelings associated with your grief you will begin to recognize triggers. This in turn is a good time for positive self-talk and identifying negative thoughts and behaviors.[1]

On the *Chapter 1 Art Therapy Activity Page*, write out any emotions coming to the surface as you are grieving the loss of your baby. Draw an emoji that symbolizes each emotion.

---

[1] "Journaling for Mental Health" by Watson, Frasier, and Ballas, 2022, www.urmc.rochester.edu

Chapter 1 Art Therapy Activity Page: Messages to Myself

Chapter 2

My Story

Last night I asked the stars to bring you back to me.

— *K. Azizian*

What you are going through right now is so hard that some days you won't feel like getting out of bed until you've cried through an entire box of tissues. Other days, your brain may be so foggy you won't be able to hold a meaningful conversation. Even your partner and best friends cannot possibly have the right words because you are convinced there are none to be said.

How do I know this to be true? Because I went through this awful reality myself. I've had three miscarriages. My first was at the age of 24, too young to realize how such an event would send me spiraling for months. I was feeling depressed, confused, guilty, angry, and so much more. My dreams of going from a positive pregnancy test to holding my baby were no longer relevant. I would never know what color my baby's eyes would be. His personality traits. What he would grow up to become. Those things were no longer there to dream about.

What now?

There was a raw, ugliness to my grieving. I would cry in my closet. Secretly go to baby stores to look at the tiniest of sleepers and imagine, *what if?* I would do anything just to feel closer to the baby I lost. I wished so hard that I was dreaming, and the baby was still safely in my womb. I didn't want to put it behind me. My way of moving on was to continue nurturing the love I had for my lost baby. I felt I had this hole in my soul. Everyone should see it.

Why weren't they seeing it?

The days and months to follow were messy. I was up. I was down. Cloudy one day, sunny the next. My grief didn't follow steps or a timeline. There wasn't a list with boxes to check off. If there were, some boxes would have been checked hundreds of times, until the paper tore. I didn't know if this was normal, or if I was in a depressed emotional state that I would never get out of. It felt as if I were drowning, and no one was there to save me.

So, I decided then that I needed to save myself.

Through this darker period of my life, I was able to make sense of it through researching how the brain reacts to grief. I studied art therapy for four years in a local university and become a certified Art Therapist. I used the information I learned there to help me better understand my own grief. On the pages that follow, I will share with you some of the information I learned about the brain and grief, as well as some of the art therapy activities that have helped me heal.

This book is a culmination of over 40 years of my life spent learning about and dealing with loss, and the grief that comes with it. It is meant to bring you understanding, hope, and most importantly, peace. The art therapy activities that follow are meant to enhance your own healing process and, along the way, create loving memories of the dreams and hopes you had for your baby.

Chapter 2 Art Therapy Activity: Your Story

On the *Chapter 2 Art Therapy Activity Page* that follows, draw a picture of what you have been going through since your loss. Like many of the pictures you draw in this book, this probably will not be a pretty one. If you feel stuck in a dark place, show that. If you are in the stages of feeling better, draw that. Scribbles and stick figures are more than okay if that's easier for you. Art therapy is not about the quality of the art, but the necessity of the healing. Date and title your drawing. Titles are important, because they can open your mind to additional exploration.

Chapter 2 Art Therapy Activity Page: Your Story

Chapter 3

The Knitted Blanket

On my silent days I miss you a little louder.

— *C.C. Aurel*

Memories of losing the three babies that I miscarried many years ago have been buried deep down in my psyche, where reminiscing doesn't dare venture. But a few months ago, something happened to cause a revelation within me regarding those miscarriages.

I read a friend's post on social media announcing that she had miscarried. I remember reading it and rereading it. I was just staring at it and trying to make sense of all the unexpected thoughts that were suddenly swarming around in my mind. I had to sit down. To process this.

Of course, my first thought was how sad I felt for my friend and her family. But there was more to it. My thoughts centered around how odd it felt for me to *see* such news being announced publicly. How others were giving their condolences, and some were even sharing that they had miscarried, as well. I was scrolling through the comments like a crazy woman. I had to sit down. Tears started flowing down my cheeks. *Where was this coming from?* I was stunned when I realized what I felt, deep down, was shame and anger.

My mind went back to the times when I had miscarried. Now, for the first time, I realized I did something wrong. Or rather, I didn't do something right. I remembered so clearly how, after each miscarriage, I suppressed my sadness, my grief, to the point where I suppressed the memory of my lost babies and the dreams I had of their lost futures. And I did it quickly, because I felt my grief made everyone else feel uncomfortable. There was no public sharing of what happened, no village to hold me up. That's just how society was at that time. I didn't even think to name my babies, write down their due dates, or the dates I miscarried. I wanted to scream for going so many years trying to not think about my sweet angels. I felt I let my babies down.

As my anger subsided, I realized, *this is ridiculous*. Almost four decades later, I am just now seeing what should have happened years ago. The group of people commenting on that social media post? That group was so tight knit and supportive that I could almost see my friend being hugged and comforted by them. That revelation has brought me here, to write this book and urge everyone to join me in The Knitted Blanket movement.

Why The Knitted Blanket? When healthy babies are born in the Midwest where I am from, it is a tradition for some hospitals to give out tiny, knitted hats and blankets to newborns. When the baby outgrows them, the parents tuck them away in a keepsake box, to look upon lovingly, once in a while, as the years pass. But for those who have lost a baby before reaching full-term? There is usually nothing. Nothing tangible to hold in the future as a way to memorialize and feel closer to the baby that was lost.

The time is now to do something about that. Because every parent who has lost a baby should have a village to console and support him or her. Because every parent should have something to hold tight as they remember their sweet baby.

To those who have lost an unborn baby, this book is for you to create memories as you heal through art and journaling activities.

For those who know someone that lost a baby, I invite you to read this book to better understand what your loved ones are going through. I urge you to give them a knitted baby blanket. To symbolize how we, as a society, can be a tight knit community that blankets them in love and support.

Chapter 3 Art Therapy Activity:
Knitted Blanket Collage

Choose images from magazines that you find calming, soothing, and even meditative. On the *Chapter 3 Art Therapy Activity Page,* combine the images to create a collage to represent inner peace. Draw a blanket under your images to represent the support you feel from that inner peace.

Chapter 3 Art Therapy Activity Page: Knitted Blanket Collage

Chapter 4

What is Art Therapy?

I found that I could say things with color and shapes that I couldn't say any other way.

— Georgia O'Keefe

It's hard to fathom that the earliest drawings by humans were made around 45,000 years ago. Some experts assert that the drawings were made to represent the beliefs and practices of their time.[2] Others believe they represent the beginning of an early form of language development.[3] Whatever the reason, the power exists within us to want to draw and create to express and communicate ideas. Art has long been used to express many emotions, including loss, grief, and mourning. It's through this natural form of expression that we can begin to understand our thoughts and emotions a bit better.

---

2 www.history.com

3 www.britannica.com

When I was studying to become a certified Art Therapist, I couldn't wait for each new assignment I was given. I was not only intrigued by the art therapy activities we learned to use with clients, but also how I would complete the activities personally. I was amazed at how my mark-making brought my thoughts and emotions to the surface and took me out of my comfort zone. I thought the activities were like magic in that they made me acutely in tune with my own self-awareness. I felt like a child again, drawing for inner reflection, not outward beauty. Creating art can be both inspiring and stimulating for the mind.

Art therapy is a way to use visual expression to connect feelings with thoughts. By creating a tangible product, one is able to record her own feelings and experiences, making it easy to look back and see the progress of healing. There is an inherent healing power in the creative process, and it has been proven to increase brain levels of serotonin, which is known to help with depression.

There are two main types of art therapy. The first is Clinical Art Therapy. This should be facilitated in-person by a licensed Art Therapist in order to work in a formal capacity. Art Therapists design specific, guided art-based projects to meet the needs of each individual client. Questions about the client's art are posed to help the client better understand her thoughts and emotions. Goals are then created based on the Art Therapist's diagnosis, established both through the art and the client's remarks. The Therapist then sets up a plan of action to help the client overcome some challenges she may have.[4]

---

4 https://www.rtor.org

The other type of art therapy is Self-guided Art Therapy. You don't necessarily need to see an Art Therapist to experience some of the therapeutic benefits of artistic expression. Self-guided Art Therapy is when the process of creating the art is the therapy, not the end product. One can, of course, look at her own finished artwork and make some personal assumptions and have "ah-ha" moments about what was created. But the main reason to do Self-Guided Art Therapy is for personal exploration and self-understanding. It's a way to express your emotions without talking, and process complex feelings to find relief. It's giving voice to something there may be no words for.[5]

You don't have to be a talented artist to participate in either kind of art therapy. Once you unleash your creativity, your inner artist will quickly wake up. You will realize that the art doesn't have to be pretty, just a reflection of your thoughts and emotions. Sometimes those can be messy and confusing. Just like life itself.

Your mind needs to become quiet for a while. Get absorbed in the moment. Be spontaneous. Try not to get distracted by what you are drawing. Let the art take its own shape as you create it. After a few drawings, you should find the process itself relaxing and relieving your stress as you go.

Darcy Lynn, a cancer survivor who used art therapy to cope with her illness, said, "Painting provided the one control I had of my situation. No one could tell me how or what to paint. Doctors controlled my body, but I controlled my soul. Painting offered me a world of my making—an escape from the angst, yet, at the

---

5 https://www.rtor.org

same time, a way for me to show myself what was happening and how strong I was."[6]

The art therapy activities in the following chapters are meant to help you escape your grief through expressing how you feel in your art and reflect on those feelings in order to help you heal, move on, and maintain a healthy mind-set. The goal is for you to express yourself and see what emerges from your mark-making. There are no rules. Logic doesn't have to exist in those marks.

As far as art supplies for the activities go, they can be as simple as pencils, crayons, or markers. But if you want to paint, use glitter, or any other art medium, go for it! It really doesn't matter what supplies you choose to use as long as you are comfortable using what you have.

Magazines or printed images found online will be needed for some of the activities. You can also use these to gather alphabet letters and quotes to add to your work.

An optional suggestion is to listen to music while you create. You can even make playlists for different mood vibes in order to really set the scene for creating.

---

6 Art Therapy Sourcebook

Chapter 4 Art Therapy Activity: Draw THAT Feeling

Loss can create a whole host of feelings. Some are more lingering, while others are fleeting. To start this activity off, do a mindful check-in. Close your eyes and take a deep breath. Being honest with yourself, think about what feeling you think is holding you back on your healing progress. Confusion? Depression? Guilt or shame? Whatever it is, bringing it to the forefront of your mind can help you purge that feeling.

On the *Chapter 4 Art Therapy Activity Page*, draw a picture of yourself feeling *that* emotion you thought of. The one that's holding you back. Once you are done, paint or color over it! As if you are getting rid of it forever. This literal act of making the image disappear can help you visualize that negative energy leaving your mind and body.

Chapter 4 Art Therapy Activity Page: Draw THAT Feeling

Chapter 5

Stages of Grief and Loss

Grief is just love with no place to go.

— Jamie Anderson

L et's take a peek at the ugliness of grief, so we can better understand it. Put in the simplest of terms, grief is an intense emotional experience triggered by a loss. According to WebMD, "Grief is a natural response to losing someone or something that is important to you. You may feel a variety of emotions, like sadness or loneliness. Everyone grieves differently. But if you understand your emotions, take care of yourself, and seek support, you can heal."[7]

My miscarriages happened before the internet was a thing for the masses. I didn't have information at my fingertips like we do now. So, I tried to get my hands on as many books as possible that would explain what was going on inside my head and heart after losing my first baby. Unfortunately, I had a hard

---

7 https://www.webmd.com/depression/guide

time finding books with the information I was seeking. I do remember finding a book that explained that there are common steps people go through when they suffer a loss. Humans crave connection in all facets of life, and it made me feel better knowing I was harboring feelings others had also experienced during the grieving process.

These steps are called the Stages of Grief.[8] The first "grief model" was developed by Elisabeth Kubler-Ross in 1969. She became notable for this model after publishing her book, *On Death and Dying*. Kubler-Ross believed the stages were denial, anger, bargaining, depression, and acceptance. Her research findings held true for many years. But as time passed, others began to question Kubler-Ross's model. The emotions listed in her model were very real, but some asserted the fact that she stated them as being sequential was not realistic. Others felt more emotions should be included. While her model is still used by many, over the years the models have changed according to research and modern opinions. Currently, there are still several varying opinions on what the stages of grief might look like, and even which emotions should be considered in those models. It would make sense to state there are as many "models of grief" as there are people grieving. Everyone handles it differently, and there are different circumstances surrounding each loss. Grieving is not a tidy process. One does not end one stage completely before going on to the next. It is often a back-and-forth process as the mind tries to figure out how to handle the grief. But there are some commonalities in the stages of grief and the order of emotions experienced.[9]

---

8 https://www.healthline.com/health/stages-of-grief#7-stages
9 https://drsarahallen.com/miscarriage/

To understand, as a baseline, what each emotion is, let's first look at their meanings:

- **Shock and Denial**: This is a state of disbelief. You many feel numb as your brain tries to process the loss. *This can't be happening.*

- **Pain and Guilt:** You may feel that the loss is unbearable, and you're making other people's lives harder because of your feelings and needs. *I feel bad that I bring up my sadness to my friends, ruining their good mood.*

- **Anger:** This may be directed toward your body for letting you down, or others that don't seem to understand the grief you are feeling. It could also be aimed at medical professionals who you feel didn't do enough to help. *How could you fail me like this?*

- **Bargaining:** This stage is when your brain starts to try to rationalize what happened and questions "What if" and "If I had only..." Often blame and anger are related to this stage, so it's important to remember that you didn't do anything to cause this. Pregnancy loss and complications can happen to anyone, and most often the reasons for the loss remain unknown. *If I had just stopped working so hard, this would not have happened to me.*

- **Depression:** As you process and reflect on the loss, you may feel you need to be alone. However, loneliness and feeling isolated, resulting in withdrawing from everyone in your life, may occur. Crying, shame, and even hopelessness may be felt in this stage. *I just can't get out of bed...no one else understands how I feel.*

- **The Upward Turn**: When your anger and pain begin to diminish, this stage can find you in a more calm and relaxed state. *My loss was real and intense, but there are still good things in my life that need my attention.*

- **Reconstruction and Working Through:** You feel like you are moving forward, as the pieces of your life begin to come back together. *I have crawled through the darkest days, and now I can use the strength I have gained to regroup.*

- **Acceptance and Hope:** Gradual acceptance is taking place, and your thoughts are no longer consumed by your loss. You are getting used to your new way of life and see the future in a more positive light. It's important to remember that there isn't a time frame for how long it takes to reach acceptance. You need to give yourself plenty of time to heal, which means you shouldn't put pressure on yourself to go faster than you are ready to. Deal with the grief as it comes. *My future isn't what I imagined it would be. It's time for me to write a different story for myself.*

Chapter 5
Art Therapy Activity:
Relax With Scribbles

Scribble drawing is a popular technique in art therapy. It is often used to calm the mind and help in the relaxation process. It's used for both adults and children, because the subject matter is random and requires no premeditated ideas of what should be drawn on the paper. There is no right or wrong way of doing this, making it stress-free in terms of not needing to imagine what the end product will look like.

Begin by choosing any color of crayon or marker and put it in your nondominant hand. Now, take a deep breath and put the utensil on *Chapter 5 Art Therapy Activity Page.* Loosely draw all over the paper using a continuous line, curving around spontaneously. As you do this, set your gaze to where your crayon is leaving the mark. Focus on the immediate present only. The here and now. Take a break from all of the thoughts and worries going through your mind. Look at the mark you're making. Realize you are making marks that are creating something that didn't exist before now. *You* are in control.

You have the power to make the marks go in any direction you want. Make more continuous marks in other colors. Use any colors you are unconsciously compelled to use. Add as many or few colors as you want.

An optional addendum to this exercise is to come back to this later and color in the shapes you created with your lines. This is another activity that can help you just let your mind wander as you color, releasing any thoughts you don't want to keep.

Chapter 5 Art Therapy
Page: Relax With Scribbles

Chapter 6

The Symptoms of Loss and Grief

What cannot be said will be wept.

— *Sappho*

Whatever you are feeling now is a normal, natural response to your recent pregnancy loss. You may find that you can't stop crying or that, no matter how hard you try, are unable to shed a single tear. Maybe you can't seem to muster up enough energy to make yourself dinner, or you are cooking your tail off in the kitchen when it is isn't necessary to. Whatever your response is to the loss is just that—yours. Take whatever time you need to process what you just went through. It's *your* journey.

After a miscarriage the emotional impact usually takes longer to heal than the physical recovery will. It's just as important to take care of your emotional self as it is your physical body, and both parts of you need to heal in this time.

According to Dr. Sarah Allen, typical anxiety and depression symptoms following a pregnancy loss can include:

- Depressed or irritable mood for most of the day
- Anger outbursts or irritability
- Withdrawal from family and friends and other social interactions
- Difficulty falling and staying asleep
- Feelings of shame, guilt, and inadequacy
- Difficulty concentrating and making decisions
- Coping with stress through unhealthy behaviors, such as excessive drinking or eating
- Ruminating over what has happened
- Spending excessive time online researching miscarriage and other health concerns

For some people, the symptoms of depression or anxiety are long-lasting. These symptoms can interfere severely with day-to-day activities. This could be attributed to Acute Stress Disorder. ASD can occur within the first month of a traumatic event, such as a pregnancy loss. Some symptoms of Acute Stress Disorder are:

- Sense of numbness or lack of emotional responsiveness
- Feeling dazed or outside of oneself
- Inability to recall aspects of the trauma
- Reliving the event through recurrent thoughts, dreams, or flashbacks
- Avoiding anything that is a reminder of the loss of the baby
- Persistent edginess and/or distress

If you are impacted by continued symptoms listed above and feel stuck, it's important to remember you are not alone in this. Professional support is one way to help you move forward. Your OBGYN may be able to refer you to local mental health professionals who are trained in this specific area of grief and loss.[10]

During my own healing process, I went through many of the above emotions. I felt alone in dealing with them because it was so hard for me to articulate to others all the thoughts and emotions swirling in my head. Looking back, I feel there were two main reasons that stood in the way of being able to move forward in my healing.

First, I didn't feel like I could discuss the loss with anyone other than a counselor. Talking about my miscarriages to others seemed so difficult, and not just for the reason you may be thinking. Yes, my heart hurt just hearing the word "miscarriage" come out of my mouth. But the main reason it was so hard? The topic was, and still is, such a taboo subject. It made others uncomfortable, so it was often easier for me to pretend I was okay and did not open up about my loss. And if I did venture into the topic, most would unknowingly minimalize it. I would hear statements like "It just wasn't meant to be." "At least you know you can get pregnant now," and "They are in a better place." I know most people meant well, but it was hard to show grace to those who, to me, seemed to downplay my loss. The lack of validation made me hesitant to reach out to anyone.

Findings from a recent study helped to prove that there needs to be more done to help others understand how to

---

10 https://drsarahallen.com/miscarriage/

console those who are grieving after losing a baby. Professor of Gynecology Tom Bourne, through the National Institute for Health and Care, conducted studies to better understand the mental health impact on women who have miscarried. Bourne found that "Society has allowed early pregnancy loss to be shrouded in secrecy, and not really acknowledged or thought about in terms of a traumatic event." He noted that very few studies, if any, examined post-traumatic stress in relation to miscarriage. Bourne goes on to say that the studies were made "to investigate the issue, and because we had noticed a level of psychological distress among our patients in clinical practice. We wanted evidence to quantify this."[11] One can only hope that studies like these will help others understand how emotionally traumatic a miscarriage can be.

It is important to take a moment to highlight Bourne's poignant observation, that "Society has allowed pregnancy loss to be shrouded in secrecy." As much as I want to avoid utilizing statistics—because each of us is unique—it is important to understand that even though one in four women experience miscarriage, it *still* seems too misunderstood to talk about. I believe people's hearts are usually in the right place, but most just don't know what to say and how to go about walking through the trenches with someone who has lost a baby.

Because my miscarriages happened so many years ago. I am amazed that I am just now beginning to witness women boldly discussing their losses to the masses. It seems that today's culture is getting more accepting of conversations about this. Mostly thanks to social media, women are beginning to

---

11 https://evidence.nihr.ac.uk/alert/pregnancy-loss-post-traumatic-stress.

support and comfort others who have lost babies more openly. It's a beautiful trickle-down effect. When one person shares a post about the tragedy, others comment that they have that in common. More and more comments and questions transpire, and before you know it, the whole village is on board to help, console, and just plain be there for other women who are dealing with the heartache of losing a baby. Use these social platforms to help you! Find others who are going through what you are experiencing. Learn from those hard conversations and lean into the grief.

The second reason I felt lost in my journey of healing was that there were no memories that were palpable. Mourning the loss of an unborn baby is different than that of losing a family member or friend that we have treasured moments with. In sharing a past with someone we lost, we have those memories of mutual experiences, photos, and more that are tangible in terms of dealing with loss. Friends and family have also shared those experiences and are able heal by talking with each other about the same loved one who passed. When the loss is an unborn baby, the grieving is different in that we are mourning the loss of experiences you've only dreamt about. This includes imagining what your child would be like, or what kind of a mother you would have been.

It is hard for society in general to truly understand the depth of emotions that miscarriage and stillbirth can bring. This can increase feelings of isolation and loneliness. A national survey on how the public perceives miscarriage found that around 41% of respondents felt alone after the miscarriage happened. In relation to this, years ago women often miscarried and never even knew they were pregnant. Now, pregnancy can be detected only hours after conception. This can make it difficult to suffer a loss, because there was more time to bond with the baby and dream about the future.

Chapter 6 Art Therapy Activity 1: Grief and Its Opposite

Sometimes when we lose someone, we have feelings that take up too much space in our lives. Ignoring those feelings can only make it worse in the long run. Facing those feelings head-on and actively dealing with them will help you get through the grieving process. This activity is designed to help you with that.

Divide the *Chapter 6 Art Therapy Activity 1 Page* into two columns by drawing one line starting at the top, center and ending at the bottom. Write the word "Grief" on the top of the left side column and "It's Opposite" on the right-side column.

Think about what you feel, think, or do differently now since your loss. Draw these in small pictures in the "Grief" column. In the "It's Opposite" column, draw the opposite of each picture. Date and title your work. Take time to reflect on both columns and see if there is something in the opposite column you should be focusing on.

Chapter 6 Art Therapy Activity 1 Page: Grief and Its Opposite

Chapter 6 Art Therapy
Activity 2: Make a Memory

My first miscarriage happened so quickly and unexpectedly that I was in a mental fog for a long time just trying to come to grips with it. Because of this, I didn't have the foresight to write down certain information that I now wish I had. It is hard to hang on to memories when there are few to remember, but I wish I would have written down the baby's due date. And even the date I miscarried. Although I didn't know the gender of my heavenly babies, I am still unsure as to why I didn't think to name them. As I began writing this chapter, I decided that it's never too late. I recently wrote down each name and decorated around it. The act of doing this made me smile and feel at peace with the one regret I still hung on to.

On the *Chapter 6 Art Therapy Activity Page*, add any information you want to help you remember certain things about your sweet angel, no matter how long you carried him or her. Decorate around the outside of the page.

Chapter 6 Art Therapy Activity 2 Page: Make a Memory

Chapter 7

Love Your Beautiful Self

Climb the mountains and get their good tidings. Nature's peace will flow into you as sunshine flows into trees. The winds will blow their own freshness into you and the storms their energy, while cares will drop off like autumn leaves.

— *John Muir*

After losing a pregnancy, it may feel like your world is falling apart. Even ordinary tasks, like sleeping and eating, are suddenly hard to do. If you are experiencing these challenges, be patient. Your body is vulnerable when recovering from all of the physical and hormonal changes associated with losing a baby. And to top it off, you are also grieving that loss. Grief will reside in your mind until it can be processed and worked through.

The following self-care tools[12] can help you heal from the grief by increasing your focus on resting and rejuvenating your

---

12 https://drsarahallen.com/miscarriage/

body. It's essential to take care of yourself through this difficult time. Be forgiving and kind to yourself. Even little things, like sipping tea and sitting in the sun, can be therapeutic and healing.

- **Get enough sleep**

Fatigue is one of the most obvious symptoms of grieving. And one of the most common experiences of grief is having trouble sleeping. It may be hard for you to fall asleep at night because you can't turn off all your thoughts about your loss. Consciously allowing yourself to grieve can help your brain calm down enough to fall asleep. But sometimes acknowledging your grief won't be enough. So, what then?

There are several behaviors and habits that can help you fall asleep at night and stay asleep. One such habit is to cut down on your caffeine intake. While you may want to drink coffee or soda during the day to help you stay awake, it can be counterproductive when you want to fall asleep.

- **Avoid alcohol use**

Cutting out alcohol can also be effective in improving sleep quality. Heavy drinking can cause us to spend more time in deep sleep and less in the Rapid Eye Movement (REM) stages of sleep. REM is a vital, restorative stage of sleep. In addition, alcohol can make physical symptoms worse in the morning due to dehydration and other hangover-related symptoms.

- **Follow a schedule**

Going to bed at the same time every night and getting up the at same time every morning helps your body get used to knowing when to sleep. Also, doing the same things every night before bedtime can help improve your sleep throughout the night. This can be as simple as taking a shower, brushing your teeth, and reading a book.

- **Screen-free Time**

To increase the quality of your rest, avoid screen time such as TV or your phone at least an hour or two before bed. Exposure to blue light before bed can generate alertness. Try quiet, calm activities instead like reading, knitting, or journaling.

Other simple things that may help before bed are drinking decaffeinated hot tea, using a sound machine, or applying lavender-scented lotion to your hands and face.

Chapter 7 Art Therapy
Activity 1:   Sweet Dreams

What is one idea from the previous list that you will try to get a better night's sleep?

Draw that idea on the *Chapter 7 Art Therapy Activity 1 Page*. Add those 'z's above your head! Date and title your drawing. If you are having trouble doing what you've drawn, look at it daily to remind you.

Chapter 7 Art Therapy
Activity 1 Page:
Sweet Dreams

• Exercise

Another way to practice self-care is to exercise. It not only helps you stay physically healthy, but it is great for emotional release. While exercising, endorphins are produced in the body, which are good for combating the feelings of depression and anxiety. Ask your doctor or midwife what is recommended for the type of exercise you should do if you are still feeling physically unwell. Dialing back on your normal pre-pregnancy routine may be necessary.

It is important to note that strenuous exercise could hinder the internal healing process, so begin with some light exercises, like walking. Walking can help ease muscle tension and allow you to sleep better. Walking alone can help you to process complex and painful emotions.[13]

An added bonus to the health benefits of walking is that when done with your partner, a close friend, or family member, it can make it easier for you—and for them—to talk more openly about what has happened. Breathe in the fresh air and smell the flowers together. Seeing others go about their day, alive and well, may be just the thing to remind you that you are right there too, putting one foot in front of the other.

With your doctor or midwife's permission, ease into more strenuous forms of exercise when you feel ready. After losing a baby, the body's pelvic area is going through some healing of its own. Doing exercises that focus on the pelvis can help speed up the process. However, such activities should only be done after any stitches have healed. Don't put any added

---

13 Huberty et al, 2014 – complete footnote for accuracy

pressure on yourself to exercise before your body is ready to do so.

Most importantly, exercise for the positive way it makes you feel, not as a means to lose weight. That will come in time.[14]

---

14 https://www.babycentre.co.uk/a1014806/gentle-exercise-after-pregnancy-loss

Chapter 7 Art Therapy
Activity 2: I'm a Star!

Draw a picture on the *Chapter 7 Art Therapy Activity 2 Page* of you doing your favorite exercise. Don't have one? Look online for simple exercising ideas.

Remember how it made you feel when you received a star from your teacher? Well, reward yourself! Draw stars around your drawing every time you exercise. Make it fun and use a gold pen. Date and title your drawing.

Chapter 7 Art Therapy Activity 2 Page: I'm a Star!

• **Find your happy place**

Never underestimate the value in finding your "happy place." Many find solace in going somewhere they feel the most comfortable so they can relax and clear their head. A place that fills their internal bucket and brings some joy to their day. Maybe your happy place is somewhere peaceful. Your bathtub, a quiet museum, or library.

Going to the movie theater is also a great place to go if you want to be around others but don't want to talk. Lose yourself in the plot. Free your mind from feelings that are difficult to deal with.

If you are one that thrives when surrounded by noise and the company of others, how about a theme park, arcade, shopping mall, or busy coffeeshop? Or, hop on a public bus or train, put on your headphones, and take in some city views if you are wanting to escape your normal reality for a bit. Allow your mind to wander so you can purge some of your sadness.

Going to a public pool or a natural body of water is another great option. Focus on the water. Float and feel how freeing your weightlessness can be. But before you go into the water, make sure you are at least two weeks out from losing the baby, so you won't get an infection. Talk to your doctor or midwife to see if you are ready for swimming.[15]

---

15 https://uihc.org/educational-resources/miscarriage-care-instructions-expectant-management

Chapter 7 Art Therapy
Activity 3: My Happy Place

On the *Chapter 7 Art Therapy Activity 3 Page,* draw yourself in your happy place. Use color to make it even more imaginable. Make sure you draw a smile on your face. Date and title your drawing.

Chapter 7 Art Therapy
Activity 3 Page:
My Happy Place

• Go outdoors

Another happy place, but one that deserves to be highlighted, is go out in nature! We *are* nature. Why do you think it feels so good to be surrounded by all things nature-made? We instinctively turn to the outdoors and participate in such activities as way to enhance our well-being and promote healing.

It has been scientifically proven that we are physically and mentally healthier when we are interacting with nature regularly.[16] Researchers found that people who walked in nature had lower heart rates, indicating more relaxation and less stress than their counterparts who walked only in urban settings. This study as well as other similar ones provide evidence[17] that being in natural spaces somehow soothes us, and helps us to be more open to creativity and problem-solving. These two things can be contributed to healing from trauma faster.

Dr. Kirsti A. Dyer said it best, "Time spent outdoors can be restorative and healing. Whether running through a canyon, walking on the sunny beach, hiking through a fern-filled forest, scrambling over rocks along a creek side, watching the last few rays of the setting sun, strolling along a moonlit night, or just sitting breathing fresh clean air, being out in nature is one of the best prescriptions for overall health and encouraging

16 https://www.stibbards.co.uk/latest-news/using-nature-to-help-you-through-grief/
17 http://www.takingcharge.csh.umn.edu

healing."[18] But it doesn't have to be an expansive amount of green or blue space to have these positive effects. City parks, gardens, fountains and other similar, smaller spaces can help us to be distracted from our worries.

18 https://www.stibbards.co.uk/latest-news/using-nature-to-help-you-through-grief/

Chapter 7 Art Therapy Activity 4: Walking in a Field of Flowers

Can't go outside to enjoy nature? Visualization calms and centers the mind. It can be used to create a safe and peaceful mental place for taking a break when needed.[19] Fully engaging all of your senses in this activity makes it more real and powerful. Try it! Close your eyes and visualize yourself walking in a field of flowers. What colors do you see? How do the flowers smell? How does the grass feel beneath your bare feet? Now, open your eyes, and on the *Chapter 7 Art Therapy Activity 4 Page*, draw what you saw when your eyes were closed. Give it a title when finished.

---

19 www.caps.byu.edu>visualization

Chapter 7 Art Therapy Activity 4 Page: Walking in a Field of Flowers

• Yoga

Practicing Yoga is another great form of self-care. Taking just fifteen minutes out of your day to do something you enjoy, like Yoga, can make a big difference. If you are not familiar with Yoga, simply go to any online source like YouTube, Instagram or Tik-Tok and find a video explaining some simple, introductory Yoga exercises.

There is actually a specific type of Yoga called Grief Yoga. This type of Yoga helps to address the symptoms of grief because it focuses on mind, body, and spirit, the three areas where grief manifests.[20] It combines various forms of Yoga, movement and breathing. It does this by bringing the mind to the present, helping relieve stress and anxiety.[21]

Grief Yoga is less about the physical aspect of the practice, but rather more about the emotional freedom that follows as a result. "Our mind, body, and spirit are so intimately linked that everything we experience is stored within us. Oftentimes, aches and pains and illness that seemingly come out of nowhere have an emotional, psychological, or spiritual root, and coming back to our body can induce great healing."[22]

Practicing Yoga is all about letting go of emotional pain and reconnecting to self-love and awareness.

---

20 www.adec.org
21 cruse.org.uk
22 "Finding Joy Through Movement;" https://www.blackzen.com

Chapter 7 Art Therapy
Activity 5: Yoga and You

On the *Chapter 7 Art Therapy Activity 5 Page*, draw a picture of you practicing Yoga in your home or gym. Focusing on this drawing can help inspire and motivate you into trying yoga. Date and title your drawing.

Chapter 7 Art Therapy Activity 5 Page: Yoga and You

• **Meditation**

Meditation is another form of self-care that helps the mind and body find refuge in this time of great change. It is a way to deal with the complex experience of grief you are going through without judgement or reaction, and at the same time will cultivate compassion for yourself.[23]

Experts in the field of grief espouse the benefits of meditation. "Research studies confirm that the practice of meditation and mindfulness changes our brains and our lives; reduces pain, anxiety, confusion and stress; boosts the immune system; and increases concentration, focus, and compassion, among its many other benefits. In addition, the practice of meditation and mindfulness can assist us in healing our grief, because it helps us live in the present," agrees Mary Friedel-Hunt, MA LCSW.

Meditation can help improve your sleep, when your thoughts are on repeat and keeping you up at night. It can also help with the physical symptoms you are experiencing while grieving, like headaches and muscle tension. You are more likely to stay healthy when practicing meditation while your body is dealing with the complex feelings of grief. It creates mental resilience and a barrier against stress, and therefore you become less reactive. This leads to you connecting more deeply with your inner wisdom and insight. It helps you respond to what your body and mind truly need as you are practicing self-compassion.

---

23 https://www.headspace.com/meditation/grief

Some Yoga studios have specific classes on grief, utilizing meditation. This is also a great way to connect with others who are grieving like you, making you feel less alone, while also fostering compassionate for others that are in your shoes.[24]

There are many types of meditations for grief. For a beginner, the options may seem overwhelming. Try not to overthink things. Just allow yourself to feel whatever may come up. But it really can be simple once you decide on what kind of meditation best suits you. The type you choose will depend on what emotions and troubles you are experiencing most strongly. The following list can help you determine which type[25] of meditation will work best for you.

- **Guided mediation** is a great place to start when just learning how to meditate. It is usually led by a teacher, either in person, on video, or via audio means to simply relax and calm the body. Just remember, there is no right or wrong way to do it.

- **Focus and Mantra meditation** can help when you feel overwhelmed, scattered, or feel like you can't wind down before bed.

- **Mindfulness meditation** can help you bring your attention to the present moment, get to know your habits, choose where to place your attention, and savor what you have.

---

24 https://mindfulnessandgrief.com/can-meditation-help-with-grief/
25 https://mindfulnessandgrief.com/can-meditation-help-with-grief/

- **Self-compassion meditation** can help you to not be so hard on yourself, which we so often are when we are feeling the weight of grief.

- **Compassion meditation** teaches you that you are part of a wide community of like-minded humans, all who suffer, and who want to be free from suffering.

- **Contemplative meditation** can help you manage the difficult emotion of grief, plus tap into your own inner wisdom and insight.

Doubting the effectiveness of meditation? "When you experience pure meditation, you will experience a state of stillness that flows with ease. Your body will be still, resisting sensations. Your mind will be still, no longer jumping from one thought to another. And emotionally will have a sense of peace and stillness."[26]

The best way to understand the benefits of meditation is to experience it for yourself. To begin, go to a place that you feel comfortable. Look around your space and notice the objects that surround you. Take time to really see them. Their shapes, colors, sizes. Now chose one of those objects small enough to fit in your hand. Use a pen if you can't find a suitable option. Block out everything but the object you are holding. Look at the small details of this object. Focus on it, as if it were an extension of your body. Become one with it. Great! You just practiced mindfulness! Being in the moment. The present. Doing this for even one minute will create an immediate cognitive connection, which creates a calmer state of mind.

26 www.wildmind.org

Chapter 7 Art Therapy Activity 6: Meditation and Breathwork Painting

Sometimes when we are grieving, we don't have enough energy to deal with what life throws at us. We've reviewed some tools to help us get that energy back, like improved sleep, eating the right foods, and maintaining a positive attitude. But did you know when you learn to control your breathing, it can help you manage your emotions? This is called breathwork. Our emotions have their own breathing patterns. Those patterns can significantly change the state of our mind. Therefore, breathwork is a form of active meditation. Think back to the last time you were startled. It was probably hard for you to catch your breath and when you did those breaths were short in duration. When you learn to control your breathing, you can also manage your emotions.

Start this activity with a short breathwork exercise. Take a gentle, deep breath in for a count of four and exhale for a count of six or longer. Repeat this three times. Now, with paint, or any supplies you have on hand, create abstract marks on the *Chapter 7 Art Therapy Activity 6 Page.* Do not try to create anything recognizable. Allow yourself to have no expectations and let the painting come to life on its own accord without forcing anything. Don't judge your work. Remember, this doesn't need to look good for it to be useful. The peaceful, mediative state you will arrive at during this process is the goal. At the end of the activity be mindful of how you are feeling. Date and title your painting.

Chapter 7 Art Therapy Activity 6 Page: Meditation and Breathwork Painting

• Massage

Getting a massage can be more than just a relaxing self-care activity. It can also be therapeutic. Some women have negative feelings towards their body after a pregnancy loss. They may feel like it failed them, and is broken. It can even be hard for some women to look at their body in the mirror because of the letdown.

To get past these negative thoughts, take a few minutes of your time to massage your body. This can help you start to appreciate your body again. Focus on your stomach, trying to mentally connect with it again. If this is too hard, try massaging your arms or legs first. As you consciously focus on your body, say positive affirmations such as, "I am grateful for my body carrying me through each day. I am grateful for my body, and being able to hug loved ones, walk where I need to, and do the simplest of things, like hold a flower." Using essential oils, coconut oil, rose, lavender or geranium oil as you self-massage can also help calm the senses. This process may seem silly and unproductive at first. But if you keep at it, you will begin to see your negative thoughts towards your body gradually disappear.

When you feel ready, you may also want to massage your uterus if you are not bleeding or on your period. This can help relax the uterus, increase circulation to the area, and tone the tissue. There are some massage therapists that specialize in this. Or you can go online and see how you can do it yourself. Be easy on yourself and use only gentle pressure. Some emotions may be stirred up when you do this. Let them happen and feel positive knowing that they will soon be released. However, you should consult your doctor or midwife first to make sure you are physically ready for this type of massage.

Another option is a professional, full body massage. If you have experienced a first-trimester miscarriage, you should wait until there is no more bleeding before you get a massage. If the loss occurred in the second or third trimester, it is recommended you wait approximately a week after the event. To make sure your body is ready, consult with your doctor or midwife.

While there are many types of massages, you will probably want to start out with a gentle one like a Swedish massage, rather than deep tissue. Be mindful by consciously focusing on each area as it is being massaged. Take deep breaths often to allow airflow into your body. This can help promote relaxation, reduce stress, and lead to improved mental health and positive emotions.

Other types of massages are hot stone, aromatherapy, trigger point, Shiatsu, and many more. Be sure to let your Massage Therapist know what your body has gone through since the pregnancy loss so that he or she can tailor the experience to your specific physical and emotional needs.[27]

In addition to the previously mentioned self-care options, the following are a few more suggested ways to take care of yourself while navigating through grief.

- **Join a pregnancy loss group:** This can be done either in-person or on a web-based forum. There you will join others who have gone through similar experiences as you. Non-judgmental support, connections, and helpful information and resources are some benefits to finding

---

27 https://www.bettinarae.com/how-to-heal-your-heart-after-a-miscarriage/ ;https://natural-fertility-info.com/after-a-miscarriage.html

a support group. In the back of this book, you will find a few related support group resources.

- **Avoid big life changes:** These include such major stressors like moving, starting a new job, or making life-altering decisions. Making changes may feel like the answer when wanting to escape the pain grief and loss. But experts agree that waiting a year to make big decisions is probably a good idea. Of course, in some situations, waiting that long may not be feasible, so if big decisions must be made, do your best to weigh all options and not choose rashly.

- **Practice patience:** While grieving a loss, you may experience changes in routine, lifestyle and habits. Your thought processes and your mental and emotional state of mind can be impacted by grief. Be patient with yourself as your thinking becomes clearer, and take your time making important decisions.

- **Talk it out:** Whether to a religious or spiritual leader, a counselor or therapist, or close friends and family, give voice to your thoughts for another way to practice self-care.

Greif is a normal part of life. If you are experiencing grief, you may not necessarily need to seek medical or psychological help. But talking to a professional who can offer non-judgmental advice and support can be very beneficial in helping you move past the grief. A Grief Counselor will help you address your feelings, which can lead to identifying, expressing, and managing them in a healthy way. That person will point you in the direction of resources and support systems in your life, and help you to understand how to access them. Setting manageable goals to help you move forward should also be something that a Grief Counselor assists you with. This can be accomplished by laying out schedules that align with the goal, in order to keep moving through the grief. If you experience setbacks, the Grief Counselor can help you manage them in order to get back on track.

Chapter 8

Journaling Your Way Through It

The very act of putting pencil to paper can begin to relax you,
allow feelings to surface, and help you to put
them into a context.

— *Cathy A. Malchiodi*

A re you finding it hard to stop thinking about what has happened? When someone has experienced an event that is difficult to take in, the brain tries to make sense of it. The person may try to push away any negative thoughts associated with that event as a way to deal with them. But avoidance can sometimes make things worse. These thoughts and feelings can come out at the most inopportune times, as anger or anxiety. This grief needs a place to go! Because of this, it is best to take time to consciously process everything that is going on inside your head. Use journaling, recording your emotions in pictures, words, or both to help you do this. The very act of putting pencil to paper can begin to relax you, allow feelings to surface, and help you to put them into context.

Journaling can speed up the recovery period during sad times. Researchers found that when a person journals for 15 minutes, three days a week, for 12 weeks, they most likely would notice their feelings of well-being increase and their depressive symptoms decrease.[28]

Journaling is a great way to dive into your thoughts and feelings. To begin, find a quiet place where you won't be interrupted. I recommend turning off your TV or phone. If you aren't sure what to write, try formatting your thoughts in bullet points. This is not the place to worry about grammar, spelling, or punctuation. Just write! You can keep this journal private if you'd like, to allow yourself to honestly reflect on everything that is troubling you during your loss. Try not to censor yourself. In other words, you can write anything about the thoughts and feelings of your loss. You are in charge of whatever goes in your journal, and there is no right or wrong way to go about it. Expect to find yourself writing about negative thoughts and emotions at times. If you are feeling a bit distraught by the topic you see yourself writing, try writing about something emotionally lighter until you are ready to go back. If that doesn't work, shift how you are sitting, change your location, or go on a walk. The journal will be there when you are ready to begin again.

I began journaling years ago, after my first miscarriage, as a way to heal. My journals may be somewhat different than other people's. I'm a bit all over the place, in that I write my daily entries in the first half of the journal, and the other half is

---

28 Webmd.com

more for disjointed thoughts. For example, when I find myself feeling thankful for something as I'm journaling, I will write it on a page towards the back, and come back to it when I feel like documenting more statements of gratitude. Then I can revisit that page when I need to remind myself that my glass is half full, not half empty.

My journals are dog-eared, and have Post-it notes to mark pages I want to reread often. And of course, being an artist, I play around with mark-making and doodle all over the pages. In a literal sense, it's more of an art journal or visual journal. While it's the same as a written journal, it also incorporates images, colors, and even glued down magazine pictures and words that I am emotionally drawn to. This creative form of self-care is how I have explored and expressed my feelings over the years, and has been one of my best coping skills.

If you think keeping an art journal is something you'd like to try but believe you have little art talent, think again! All you need is a willingness to play around with art materials as you go. Even that playfulness is a healthy way to heal through creative expression. I know you will feel empowered and gain self-awareness as you look back at what you've written, drawn or glued down.[29]

---

29 https://mymodernmet.com/art-journal-ideas/; https://www.
bettinarae.com/how-to-heal-your-heart-after-a-miscarriage/

Chapter 8 Art Therapy Activity: Journal it!

A journal can be a spiral notebook, loose computer paper kept in folder, or a sketchbook or formal journal from an art store. If that's not an option, use envelopes from junk mail, or any other recycled paper. If the cover of your journal is dark or already has pictures on it, cover it with computer paper, scrapbooking paper, or any other paper you can find. Decorate the front with images or words that make you smile. If you would rather not draw anything, consider cutting out magazine pictures or using stickers to make your cover a special one. Sometimes, I take Mod Podge and brush a coat over the top of my glued down magazine pictures to cover and protect it. Just be careful—Mod Podge will smear photographs and certain computer printer inks.

Now, it's time for the first entry in your journal. Without giving it any thought, take a few short minutes and create any image. Do not worry what the drawing looks like. Next, somewhere on the same page, write down any thoughts associated with that image. This is the time to be truthful and not hold back any thoughts. Can't get a journal right now? Use the *Chapter 8 Art Therapy Activity Page*. Date and title each journal entry.

Chapter 8 Art Therapy
Activity Page: Journal it!

Chapter 9

Positive Energy and Daily *Mantras*

Be the energy you want to attract. Focus on the good.

— *Author Unknown*

You may be finding it hard to stay positive during this time. But trying to maintain positive emotions is very important in helping you cope with your loss. When you are faced with the challenge of moving on, it withdraws from your energy. Once that energy is depleted, doubt and negative thoughts seep in. Good vibes can boost one's state of well-being and help to release the feelings that grief brings to the surface.[30]

There are many ways to tap into that positive energy. One such way is using *mantras* or words of affirmation. A mantra is defined as a word or sound repeated to aid concentration in meditation. We can use *mantras* as a tool to release our mind, to

---

30 https://www.lifehack.org/569466/how-regain-your-positive-energy-when-things-are-getting-tough

free ourselves from the hurt that the mind and body is suffering through.

Think of a word, phrase, or short song lyrics that has special meaning for you at this time. As you go about your day, find moments to close your eyes and say aloud or think about your mantra. I mean, really think about. Concentrate on what it means. Especially what it means for you. The key is to repeat it often, whether it is aloud or to yourself. You can bow, chant, or sing the mantra. Close your eyes as you begin to go to sleep at night and whisper the mantra, over and over. Maintaining your mantra as the last thought of the day can be very beneficial to reinforcing your mental healing.

You could also write down your mantra on a piece of paper and keep it where you can look at it often. Put it on your computer at work or under a magnet on the fridge at home. Any way you can get those positive thoughts out in the universe will help!

Chapter 9 Art Therapy Activity: My Mantras

What do you want your mantra to be today? Choose words that will help you feel positive throughout the day. When you have your mantra picked out, use your art supplies and write out those words, utilizing colorful letters. Decorate around the words to make it look visually uplifting as well. If you don't feel like getting out art supplies, cut out letters from magazines to form the words you want to create and glue them down on the *Chapter 9 Art Therapy Activity Page* or in your journal.

Below are some mantra suggestions to help you get started:

I am calm.

I am healing from my loss.

Breathe in strength, breathe out sadness.

I trust my body.

I am not alone.

I have the power to renew my energy.

I give myself permission to stop wondering why it happened.

I deserve to savor the good things that happen today.

I am not perfect, but I am wonderful.

I am getting better every day.

Chapter 9 Art Therapy
Activity Page: My Mantras

Chapter 10

Happy on Purpose

Science confirms what we already know to be true: Your brain is constantly taking note of the emotional tone of your thoughts. When you have a lot of negative thoughts, your brain reacts by telling your body to feel stressed and sad. When you are thinking positive thoughts, you will feel happy and relaxed.[31]

Need to be reminded there are still things to be happy about? Write down as many things you can think of that make you happy. Family, the ocean, your pet...the list can go on and on.

---

31 mayoclinic.com

Chapter 10 Art Therapy Activity: Happy Self-Box

For the next step of this activity, you will need a box, magazine, glue stick, and scissors. Optional supplies: stickers, paint, markers, and washi tape. The box should have a lid, like a shoe box, a cardboard photo box from a craft store, or even a spare box you got in the mail.

Begin by going through a magazine and cutting out anything that brings a smile to your face. Try not to rationalize why you choose certain pictures or words. Just let your mind go with whatever you decide to cut out.

When you have a collection of "happy" images, begin arranging them on your box and glue them down. You can add extra embellishments to give your box pizazz. If you have leftover pictures, fill the inside of your box as well.

When your Happy Self-box is completed, take the time to look at it and let your mind wander as you focus on the images and words. Do you see a theme in what you chose? Are there any repeated images? Write down in your journal, or on the *Chapter 10 Art Therapy Activity Page,* a list of the "happy" things you see on your Happy Self-Box. When you are feeling a bit down, take a look at the box to bring a smile back to your face.

Chapter 11

Mandala

Each person's life is like a mandala—a vast, limitless circle.
We stand in the center of our own circle and everything we
see, hear, and think forms the mandala of our life.

— *Mother Pema Chodron*

Mandalas are circles in art. They are designs that radiate outward from a center point. *Mandala* is the Sanskrit word for circle, and signifies growth and the wholeness of the self. In Tibet, the mandala is called *Khyil-khor*, which refers to the center of all creation, where a truly awakened being lives, taking the meaning further than the Sanskrit reference.[32]

The mandala is one of the most universal symbols of our world. It has been used in almost all cultures over the course of many centuries. In most usages, it is a symbol of unity and oneness. We see mandalas everywhere, from Aztec calendars to North American dream catchers. They are all around us in nature, visible in snowflakes, flowers, and the center of fruits.

The mandala also symbolizes the womb, motherhood, and the act of nurturing.

In art therapy, we use this as a drawing meditation. It is used to center ourselves in times of confusion and stress. It is a way to gather our thoughts and reflect.

Chapter 11 Art Therapy Activity: Mandala

Put a small dot in the center of the *Chapter 11 Art Therapy Activity Page* or in the journal you created during chapter eight. The mandala you make can have color or be black and white. As you work out from this dot, do not worry about it being symmetrical. Our imperfections should be considered organic and beautiful. Create a slightly larger circle around the dot using more dots, shapes or lines. Continue with various circle designs as you continue this process towards the edges of the paper. When done, reflect on the wholeness of your design. Give it a title.

Chapter 11 Art Therapy
Activity Page: Mandala

Chapter 12

Crystal Ball

When thinking about life, remember this: no amount of guilt
can change the past and no amount of anxiety
can change the future.

— Author Unknown

It is in our nature as humans to think about the future. To dream and hope for the very best for us. But, when one cannot imagine a positive future due to certain life circumstances beyond our control, his or her mental health can decline. In the therapy world, cognitive distortion is when someone always assumes the worst will happen, causing reality to become distorted through a negative lens. And then those emotions begin to take over.[33]

Pregnant women naturally think about how the future will be with a new baby in it. When a loss of a baby occurs, it is very hard to move past what might have been. And even more difficult to rationally think how the future will look, knowing that specific baby won't be in it. Because feelings are at the root of any loss, art therapy can be particularly useful, helping grieving individuals express their emotions and create a new view of themselves and of life after loss.[34]

The crystal ball activity on the next page is meant for you to consciously think about the weeks and months ahead. It's a *very* hard conversation to have with yourself. You will have to think about some serious "what ifs."

"What if I can't get pregnant again?" is a common, but difficult, question after losing a baby. Of course, only time will reveal the answer. But in the meantime, focus on the positives in your life, no matter how that "what if" unfolds for you.

Chapter 12 Art Therapy Activity: Your Crystal Ball

Draw a large circle to represent a crystal ball on the *Chapter 12 Art Therapy Activity Page*. You can draw a fun base that it sits on. Divide it into three pie-like sections. In each section, draw an illustration of something positive you would like to see happen in your future that isn't baby-related. For example, if you are planning on taking a course in something you've always wanted to try, draw that. If you are wanting to take a trip somewhere, draw that. Focus on the positives, and look at them whenever you have doubts. Draw more crystal balls in your journal when there are other things you envision happening in your future as you think of them. Be mindful that not all things we envision happening will in fact come to fruition.

Chapter 12 Art Therapy Activity Page:
Your Crystal Ball

Chapter 13

Your Superpowers Are Still Here

As I reclaim my story, I fix my eyes on the Sun, who empowers me to walk in dignity.

— Proverbs 31:25

Unfortunately, there is no changing what happened, or what brought you here, reading this book on how to cope with the loss of a baby. It's especially hard because what you're going through can change your usual feelings and behaviors. Give yourself permission to cry over the sorrow of what happened, and for the fear of the uncertainty of what lies ahead. What's important is that you don't let it take your power. Don't let the pain and fear take over. You need to push through those negative thoughts in order to see the good days you know, deep down, are ahead.

The good news is that your brain has the tools to give you the ability to move forward.

Use the art therapy strategies in this book to help you. Your work will show your frustration, sadness, and disappointment. It may even bring some of it out to the forefront of your being. Think of it as being released, not magnified. Focus on one day at a time, take good care of your mind and body, and remember that you are in control. Your superpowers are still here, waiting for you to reclaim them.

If you ever feel like things are so dark that you don't think you can handle them alone, or even feel like hurting yourself, please seek the help of a professional.

Chapter 13 Art Therapy Activity: What's your Superpower?

Just because you lost a part of you, doesn't mean you lost your superpowers. You still have what made you awesome before your loss. Reflect on what superpowers you hold that you are most proud of. On the *Chapter 13 Art Therapy Activity Page,* use any art materials available, and draw yourself as a superhero. Give your superhero-self a "super" name.

Not sure how to identify your superpowers? Think about what drives you. What do people compliment you on?

Some superpower ideas to help you get started:

- Good friend
- Resilient
- Empathic
- Creative thinker
- Decisive

Chapter 13 Art Therapy Activity Page: What's your Superpower?

Chapter 14

For Friends and Family

In your dark days, just turn around and I will be there. And maybe I won't have any more light to give than what you already have. But I will take your hand and we will find the light together.

— JmStorm

There is almost no greater emotional devastation than the loss of a baby. And navigating through that loss can be difficult for all involved. If you are someone that wants to help the grieving parents, you may find it hard to know what to say or do. Supporting them does not mean you can take away their pain, but you may be able to help them get through the healing process a little easier. Providing a calming presence to let them know you are there for them is one of the most important things you can do.

If you are on the outside looking in, you may think that one can only grieve for the loss of a baby they've held. But that is simply not true. Deep grief can be felt for the loss of a baby that was still in the womb. A parent can grieve the loss of the unspoken hopes and dreams they had for the baby, no matter how many days, weeks, or months they carried it for.

To add to the grief, there seems to be a cultural discomfort when discussing the loss of a baby, and therefore women who have miscarried are often met with a wall of silence. But avoidance can be worse than saying the wrong thing, and can actually make the experience more painful. Not reaching out may lead them to believe that their loss is insignificant. One of the most important needs after a pregnancy loss is knowing people care and are thinking of them.

Before you reach out, try becoming informed of the situation. You've already made a step in the right direction by opening the pages of this book. Reading about miscarriage and bereavement is important in order to help those who are grieving. It's good to know what physical and mental obstacles each person may be encountering after the loss.

If you are planning to visit the grieving parents, do not show up unannounced. They may be resting, not feeling well, or just want to be alone. Call ahead so they can let you know a time that will work best for them. If you have children, especially babies, it may be a good idea to leave them with someone else while you visit. Many parents don't feel like being around other children after losing a baby.

Even a supportive person can have trouble finding the right words of comfort. "I don't know what to say," is better than saying nothing at all. But the best way to start off the conversation can be as simple as saying, "I'm so sorry." Continue with being honest and say something like, "I can't imagine what you are going through and how you must be feeling."

Be willing to talk about the loss. Ask, "How are you feeling today?" and give them a chance to talk about what happened. Show them you are willing to handle the conversation, no matter how difficult it may be. If you feel like crying with them, go ahead. It shows that you care. But don't break down sobbing to the point that they need to comfort you. You are there to support them.

If the grieving parents gave the baby a name and say it in conversation, do the same. That shows them that you know the baby had an identity and was a part of the family. Using the baby's name is also a good idea if you are sending a card, calling on the phone, or texting.

It's okay to bring up a similar loss of your own if you feel compelled to do so. Just be sure you are not comparing one loss to the other. Experiencing a pregnancy loss can be lonely, and hearing someone else talk about such an experience can be reassuring. Knowing someone else went through the same thing can make them feel like opening up, knowing they won't be judged or told to move on.

Phrases such as, "I know how much you loved this baby;" "Remember to be kind to yourself;" or "Our entire family grieves with you," are things you can say to be supportive and show you care.

When having a conversation, avoid mentioning the current life happenings of others, such as someone else having a baby. Hearing about others celebrating life while in a season of loss can be deeply painful. Avoid triggers such as talking about friends and their children's activities until after a few weeks of grieving have passed. Be sensitive to unexpected emotional reactions by the grieving parent, even weeks or months later.

Even those with good intentions can say things that are hurtful. Avoid cliché responses like, "At least you know you can have children." Or, "Everything happens for a reason." There is no replacing the loss of their child or attempting to explain why it happened. Such statements suggest they should put the loss behind them and forget about it. "Be strong. Don't cry," is another example of what not to say. It can make them feel like they are not doing a good job of coping. There is no right or wrong amount of time to get over pregnancy loss, and everyone should be given the space to mourn in a way that's right for them. Additionally, you should stay away from giving unsolicited advice such as, "You're stressing too much." Or "You're overthinking it." These statements are just not helpful, and can come off as insensitive.

If the baby's nursery was already set up, one common thing to avoid is suggesting that it's time to clear it out. They may not be at the point of removing it yet. But, if enough time has passed and they are permanently keeping the nursery as a shrine of sorts, it may be a sign that they are not coping well, and should seek the help of a counselor.

Other ways to show you care are with various acts of kindness. Instead of saying "If you need anything, let me know," be specific in what you can offer. Some people have a hard time asking for help or are too deep in their grief and anger to know what they want. Good, clear examples of what to say are, "I am home tonight if you'd like to talk." Or, "Would you like me to pick up any groceries for you while I'm at the store?" Texting or calling to check in is another nice way of showing you are thinking of them.

There are many gift-giving ideas that can make someone feel special while they are grieving. Here are some good suggestions:

- A gift certificate for a gentle body massage can be useful, considering the feeling of touch can be therapeutic. A massage can release the tension that grief and stress may cause.

- With grief there is usually some crying that goes on as a way to purge the sadness. Give eye masks that are made with gels that cool and soothe puffy eyes, reduce swelling, and give relief from headaches that come with crying.

- Our noses also get a bit tender when we cry. Give soft, colorfully designed handkerchiefs to let them know it's okay to cry. Essential oils to dab on the cloth is a bonus, as they can help calm the senses.

- Often, those who are grieving may not feel like cooking or taking the time to eat. Offer to make something that can be eaten simply by warming it up. Healthy, easy finger food is not only convenient, but also helps them to stay nourished. Gift cards to home food delivery services such as Uber Eats or Doordash is another helpful idea.

- If you feel like doing something that costs more or want to give as a group, gift them fun, colorful bed sheets and comfortable pajamas for the days they don't feel like getting out of bed. Buy some magazines or books to have at close reach on their nightstand. These can help to momentarily take their mind off the difficult time they are going through and help them relax.

- Create a list of movie suggestions you think they would be interested in. Pick movies without triggers, such as characters that are pregnant or dealing with other forms of loss.

- A thoughtfully-crafted note can offer support and let them know you are thinking of them. If they share your faith, a passage from the Bible may give them comfort as well.

- Other thoughtful gift suggestions are framed quotes that include comforting words, or necklaces with a charm of significance, such as the baby's birthstone or a religious symbol. There are also various comfort kits available online that can be personalized for the ones you are thinking of.

- If you want to give without spending a dime, you can volunteer to walk their dog, pick the kids up from school, or schedule appointments.

They say time heals all wounds, but the amount of time is different for everyone. Don't stop supporting parents after a few weeks. Check in often, especially on holidays like Mother's Day and Father's Day, the anniversary of the miscarriage, due date, and other significant days. Sometimes feelings can resurface unexpectedly, even years later.

Resources

- Blog.prepscholar.com – Resources for how to find a Grief Counselor

- Compassionate Friends – Provides highly personal comfort, hope, and support to every family experiencing the death of a son or a daughter, a brother or sister, or a grandchild, and helps others better assist the grieving family; resources in Spanish and other languages available

- Exhale: an After-Abortion Hotline – 1-866-439-4253

- Glow in the Woods – Discussion forum and helpful posts for parents who have lost a baby

- Griefwatch – A publisher and manufacturer of bereavement books and materials used by families and professionals around the country

- Georgetown University – *Emotional Healing after a Miscarriage: A Guide for Women, Partners, Family and Friends*

- March of Dimes – Overview of dealing with grief after the death of one's baby

- M.E.N.D. – Mommies Enduring Neonatal Death. A Christian, non-profit organization that reaches out to families who have suffered the death of a baby through miscarriage, stillbirth, or early infant death

- <u>Miscarriage for Men</u> – Website that offers directional guidance and support. A place where men, who are suffering in silence, can voice their worries, fears, and just support each other, either publicly or anonymously

- <u>Miscarriage Matters</u> – Community of parents who have experienced the loss of a child/children, willing to offer friendship and a listening ear

- <u>MISS Foundation</u> – Provides support for families struggling with traumatic grief. Family Support Packets are available with information and resources for bereaved parents, grandparents and siblings.

- <u>PALS (Pregnancy After Loss Support)</u> – Supports courageous mamas pregnant again after a loss through connection with peers, awareness in the community, education of providers, and advocacy around the world

- <u>Rachel's Gift</u> – Provides support and guidance for caregivers and families enduring pregnancy and infant loss

- <u>Return to Zero</u> – Compassionate and holistic support for people who have experienced unimaginable loss during their journey to parenthood; resources in Spanish and other languages available

- <u>Return to Zero: LGBTQIA+</u> – Support for LGBTQIA+ families

- <u>RESOLVE through Sharing</u> – For providers; a not-for-profit organization providing thought leadership, and an evidence-based yet compassion-first approach to bereavement care

- <u>SHARE</u> Pregnancy and Infant Loss Support – Mission is to provide support toward positive resolution of grief experienced at the time of, or following the death of a baby. This support encompasses emotional, physical, spiritual and social healing, as well as sustaining the family unit

- <u>Sisters in Loss</u> – Dedicated to replacing silence with storytelling around pregnancy and infant loss and the infertility of black women

- <u>Star Legacy Foundation</u> – Virtual grief support groups for family members who have experienced pregnancy or infant loss; group in Spanish available

- <u>Stillbirthday</u> – Seeks to nurture sources of perinatal bereavement, strengthen skills of healthcare professionals, and increase healthy engagement of perinatal-related needs among communities

- Stillstandingmag.com – Magazine for all who are grieving child loss and infertility

- <u>Tears Foundation</u> – Seeks to compassionately lift a financial burden from families who have lost a child by providing funds to assist with the cost of burial or cremation services. Also offers parents comprehensive bereavement care in the form of grief support groups and peer companions.

Made in the USA
Las Vegas, NV
09 February 2024

85487554R00059